CH00656100

Allah to Z: Activity Book

Islamic Activities for Ramadan and All Year Long

Sam'n Iqbal

Photography Sosan Romani Akhtar Art Direction Uzma Sabir

BROYHILL PUBLICATIONS LLC

To my family, complete.
— S.I.

Text © 2013 Sam'n Iqbal
Photography © Sosan Romani Akhtar
Art Direction Uzma Sabir

Published by Broyhill Publications LLC, McLean, VA

Library of Congress Number #2013910795
ISBN # 978-0-9895411-0-7

Printed in the United States of America
www.AllahToZ.com

Contents

RAMADAN

is a celebratory time of praying and fasting among the one billion Muslims worldwide. It is the ninth month on the Islamic calendar and begins on a different date each year.

For most Muslims, Ramadan includes fasting, abstaining from eating and drinking, until the sun goes down. During this month, Muslims avoid lying, gossiping, or being greedy and do as many good deeds as possible. It is a month of healing and caring for other people who may be less fortunate.

What about children who are too young to fast?
How can we celebrate and learn more about Ramadan?

You and your children can read the many Islamic children's books available, such as **Allah to Z: An Islamic Alphabet Book**, **The Night of the Moon: A Muslim Holiday Story** or **My First Ramadan**; create arts and craft projects; or go moon and star-gazing in the backyard, observing how the night sky changes over the month, an integral part of Ramadan.

By including your children in Ramadan routines, you help them understand the holiday and the Islamic religion. The month can be full of fun activities which highlight beautiful aspects of Islam throughout history and cultures, and will keep the entire family focused on what Ramadan is truly about.

What You'll Need:

- 4 large foam boards or one very large board that can fit 30 pockets

- 30 small 4"x4" squares of colorful felt

- Glue gun

- Fabric paint

Iftar Treat Calendar

Make Ramadan exciting and educational by counting down and celebrating the days till Eid! Fill each felt pocket with a small treat, toy, candy or sticker and have your child open one each day at Iftar time, when you break fast.

Adult Prep

Hot glue the felt "pockets" (the two sides and bottom, keeping the top open) to the foam board. On each board glue two rows of five pockets across.

Kid Assembly

Using fabric paint, write one number on each felt square from 1-30. For extra fun, practice writing the numbers in Arabic. Create a Happy Ramadan sign for the top of the board and decorate with gems, stars and stickers.

Tip: Surprise your child with a few Moon Passes that let him/her stay awake for an extra few minutes for a moon sighting!

What You'll Need:

- 1 box of whole pitted dates

- 1 package cream cheese, softened and whipped

- Plastic knife

- A small cup of almonds and a small cup of chocolate chips

· ·

Chocolate and Nut Stuffed Dates

Why do Muslims break their fast with dates?
This sweet, sticky, and delicious fruit is brimming with nutrients, vitamins, and minerals. After a long day of fasting, dates help give immediate energy while digesting slowly. They are commonly eaten at Iftar time everyday during Ramadan, as Prophet Muhammad (SAW) would break his fast with ripe dates before he would pray.

Kid Assembly

Slice each date with a slit opening at the top without going all the way through and with a grown-up watching. If there are pits, scoop them out.

With a pastry bag or a small spoon, fill each date with the cream cheese filling. Place one almond or a sprinkle of chocolate chips in the center of the date.

Cover and chill until ready to serve.

What You'll Need:

- Any size cardboard box
- White cardstock
- Wrapping paper or fabric
- Tape
- Markers
- Glue

Sadaqah Box

Ramadan is a time of giving and sharing with our friends and family. Many mosques and Muslim organizations collect a variety of goods to help those less fortunate. Create a box for your child to fill with toys, games, puzzles and dolls that can be donated to other boys and girls who have very little. Remind your child that he should give away his toys with sincerity and not ask for new toys later!

Kid Assembly

Cut the top flaps off a large cardboard box, with a grown-up watching.

Cover the box with festive wrapping paper or fabric.

On white cardstock write the words "Sadaqah Box" and glue it to the side of the box.

Decorate it any way you would like to.

Tip: Keep it in an area where your child can place the things they would like to donate in it easily. Once full, donate to your local mosque, shelter, community center and school.

What You'll Need:

- Glass jars, such as old salsa, jam and spaghetti sauce jars, washed and cleaned

- Flameless tea lights

- Rubber bands or painters tape

- A variety of colorful paint or spray paint

- Paint brushes

- Mod Podge or glue

- Glitter

Laylat al-Qadr Jar of Lights

Laylat al-Qadr is also known as the "Night of Power." It commemorates the night when Angel Gibrael revealed the Quran to Prophet Muhammad (SAW), on a night during the last 10 days of Ramadan.

Painted Jars

Wrap rubber bands of various sizes around your glasses, or painters tape. Turn your jars upside down and paint 2 coats for maximum coverage and let dry completely. Remove the rubber bands over a trash can to catch the dry paint. Once you finish removing all the rubber bands, wipe down your glasses with a wet rag and set a tea candle inside.

Glitter Jars

Mix glitter with Mod Podge or glue and paint it onto your jar, using a paint brush. Experiment with designs by putting star stickers on the jar and painting over the stickers. Once completely dry, carefully remove the stickers. Place a tea light inside the jar.

Tip: Experiment with colors on other jars! Add some gold paint to the jars to give each one a fun effect when it's seen in the daylight.

What You'll Need:

- Different color and sizes of felt fabric (larger works better)

- Pencil

- Craft knife or scissors

- Batting or stuffing

- Sewing needle and thread spools

- Decorations as desired (glitter, sequins, lace, yarn, buttons, fabric paint, iron transfer letters…)

Crescent and Star Pillows

These fun-shaped pillows are soft and cuddly and a reminder of the Holy Month all day and all night! There are so many fun shapes to make and fun ways to decorate them.

Kid Assembly

Using a pencil, draw your design – a crescent and star (see appendix) – onto the felt fabric. Or make it your own by drawing your designs freehand to create custom pillows!

With a grown-up watching, cut out your design and decorate your pillows with glitter, fabric paint, sequins, flowers, buttons, lace or silly eyes.

Have a grown-up help you sew the front and back pieces together, leaving about 2" or more of open space on the side or top.

Fill with batting or stuffing and sew the opening closed.

Tip:

Decorate a plain white pillowcase with fabric paint, sequins, pom-poms and ribbon to liven up your child's bed.

What You'll Need:

- White 8 ½ x 11 cardstock or printer paper
- Computer and printer

Random Acts of Ramadan Kindness

Infuse the Ramadan spirit by performing a Random Act of Ramadan Kindness during the 30 days of Ramadan. This is a great way to share Ramadan with your neighbors and your non-Muslim friends, and let them know that it is Ramadan. Check the website www.AllahToZ.com/activity-book for more ideas!

Kid Assembly

Print "Random Acts of Ramadan Kindness" (template found in appendix) onto white cardstock. Go around town and bring Ramadan kindness to others. Take pictures helping neighbors and friends and put together a scrapbook every year to remember how it felt to do nice things for others.

1. Bring your teacher flowers one afternoon.

2. Go grocery shopping for the sole purpose of putting it in the "Food for Families" box.

3. Feed parking meters down the street.

4. Pay other children's past due library books.

5. Buy and donate toys for your local community center, children's hospital or masjid.

6. Clean out your book collection and donate to a school library in need.

7. Send or deliver handmade cards to a nursing home.

8. Make snacks or dessert for other neighborhood children.

9. Have your grown-up list something you no longer need online for free.

10. Hand a passing child a goody bag and continue walking.

11. Hand out helium balloons to children.

12. Drop off a box of diapers and toys for a new baby.

13. Leave a set of Ramadan children's books at a mall play area.

14. Offer to buy a chocolate bar for the checkout clerk at the grocery store.

15. Take back shopping carts and hold open doors for other customers.

16. Drop off some baked goods for your local volunteer firemen.

17. Paint rainbows on 20 cards that say "Have a great day" and drop them off in your neighbors' mailboxes.

18. Pick up trash around your local park or neighborhood.

19. Donate a large bag of your old clothes to a local homeless shelter.

20. Go to a local bookstore and read a story out loud, or have your grown-up read a story to you and all the other children.

21. Collect plastic bags and recycle at your local grocery store.

22. Plant a tree.

23. Make and send your grandparents a thank you card.

24. Take flowers to your camp or school teacher.

25. Bring in the mail for an elderly neighbor.

26. Visit and volunteer at an animal shelter.

27. Bring in your neighbors' trash bins.

28. Leave kind notes for siblings in places they will find them.

29. Leave out birdseed and peanut butter stick balls for birds and squirrels.

30. SMILE at everyone you pass!

Random Acts of Ramadan Kindness

you've been Rak'd

This Ramadan season we are celebrating the days of Ramadan by performing **Random Act's of Ramadan Kindness** each day. God has blessed us and we want ___ ___re our blessing with others.

What You'll Need:

- Blue construction paper
- 8 Oreo cookies
- Blue craft foam cut in a circle
- Yellow felt in a semi-circle shape
- Craft stick or plastic knife
- Glue stick
- 8 small rectangles of white paper or card stock
- Black marker

Oreo Lunar Calendar

The beginning of Ramadan is traditionally calculated by looking up at the night sky and visibly sighting the crescent moon called hilal. At the end of the month, when hilal is seen again, Eid al-Fitr will begin. This activity is a fun (and edible) way to learn the phases of the moon throughout the month of Ramadan.

Kid Assembly

Write the eight key stages of the Moon during its revolution around the earth on the small strips of white paper (see appendix): Place the white strips, first quarter, waxing gibbous, full, waning gibbous, third quarter, waning crescent, new, and waxing crescent, in a circle going counter-clockwise, starting at 12 o'clock.

On the center of the paper, glue the blue craft foam circle, representing the Earth.

On the far right side of the paper, glue the yellow felt onto the paper, representing the Sun.

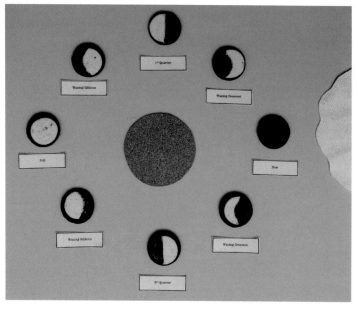

Tip:

Carefully separate the Oreo cookies. Using a craft stick, or a plastic knife with the help of a grown-up, scrape off the correct amount of white icing to make each moon phase (see picture for correct phases). Glue the correct moon phase label next to each Oreo.

What You'll Need:

- One Vase
- Small pebbles, sand or rice
- 5-8 small branches collected outside
- Green construction paper
- Pencil
- Scissors
- Glue gun or tape

Good Deed Tree

Parents are always quick to reprimand and discipline their children, but positive reinforcement goes a long way. By praising your child for their good behaviors, and having them visibly see them, it will help build their confidence and self-esteem.

Write down exceptional behaviors on the individual leaves, but leave some blank for their everyday, expected deeds. Reinforce your approval by letting your child cut out a leaf and add it to the tree each time they do a good deed.

Kid Assembly

Collect small branches off the ground. This is a great way to get some fresh air and some exercise.

Add small pebbles, sand or rice half way up your vase. This will give support to your branches when you put them in the vase.

With a pencil, draw individual leaves onto the green construction paper (or see appendix for template).

Cut out a bunch of leaves and keep them in a bowl next to your tree.

Get rewarded

Each time you do a good deed, secure one leaf onto the branch with glue or tape. For extra good behavior, write down the deed!

What You'll Need:

- Tent, or build your own with blankets
- Jar of Lights (see activity on page 12)
- Quran
- Islamic books such as Allah to Z: An Islamic Alphabet Book
- Snacks (like S'mores with halal marshmallows)
- Lot's of pillows

- -

Camping in Cave Hira

Muslims observe Laylat al-Qadr during the last 10 days of Ramadan by praying, reciting the Quran and making duas. Many stay up all night! While your child may not be able to stay up all night, instill in them the significance of Laylat al-Qadr by making it fun and eventful and a tradition to look forward to every year.

Set Up Camp

During the summer months you will be able to camp outside, for a couple hours or all night. On colder nights, you can set up camp inside your home with blankets or set up an outside tent inside.

Spend this time playing Islamic games, reading Islamic books, lounging on your Ramadan felt pillows and eating yummy snacks.

Read the Quran, pray, and make duas, remembering the significance of this holy night. This is also a good time to hear or learn some new surahs.

Quranic Arabic

Between the ages of 0-5, children absorb everything around them like a sponge!
This is why it is best to start teaching Quranic Arabic, one of the most poetic
languages in the world, to them at an early age.

The Quran is an important part of any Muslim life. It holds the complete code for
Muslims to live their lives with the commandments of Allah, taught through the
Prophet Muhammad (SAW). Memorizing parts, if not the entire Quran, is
something every Muslim strives for. And just like learning your ABCs, memorizing
the alphabet is one way to learn Arabic; then comes recognizing the letters and
learning their sounds.

Use simple lessons, games and activities to teach your children the Arabic
language, with the end goal of understanding the Holy Quran.

What You'll Need:

- 8 x 10 white wrapped canvas
- Acrylic paint
- Small or script paint brush
- Medium paint brush
- Ruler
- Pencil

Quran Canvas Art

A great way for your kids to work on their fine motor skills while practicing writing Arabic, all while learning a new surah!

Adult Prep

Using a pencil, write the chosen surah in Arabic, centered on the canvas. Or for a more simple project, trace out Allah in Arabic script.

Kid Assembly

Using a small paint brush, carefully trace over the Arabic writing with paint or trace with a marker to make it easier. Go slowly to stay in the lines. Let it dry completely.

Erase any stray pencil markings carefully once the paint is completely dry.

Tip: You can also color in any large Arabic script with a medium brush and different paint colors.

What You'll Need:

- Your favorite cookie dough recipe or pre-made cookie dough

- Cookie sheet

Arabic Alphabet Cookies

Practice the Arabic Alphabet with this fun and edible activity!

Kid Assembly

Preheat the oven to 350 (F) degrees. On a cookie sheet, create the Arabic letters with the cookie dough.

Bake for 8-10 minutes with a grown-up watching.

 Tip: Bake a shorter time for thin cookies, add time for thicker cookies.

What You'll Need:

- Wooden Arabic alphabet blocks
  (see appendix), or make your own
  blocks with 1" foam cubes (see
  appendix) and permanent marker

- A bag or bucket

· ·

Alphabet Scavenger Hunt

Get outside and make learning interactive with a fun scavenger hunt
for all the letters in the Arabic alphabet.

Search for Letters

Have a grown-up hide all the Arabic letter blocks around the
yard or inside if the weather is bad.

Find all the letter blocks and call out the name and/or sound
of the letters as you find them.

Collect the blocks in a bag or bucket.

What You'll Need:

- Colorful sidewalk chalk
- A sidewalk or driveway

Arabic Hopscotch

Incorporate learning into an active game and keep your child focused by having them up and moving around with a game of hopscotch! Have your child hop, skip and jump their way through a maze of Arabic alphabet letters drawn with sidewalk chalk, calling out each letter as they land on it.

Hop To It

Draw a hopscotch outline and fill it in with letters from the Arabic alphabet. Hop through the alphabet by saying each letter you land on.

Make the game a little harder by tossing a stone onto one of the letters, then go through the alphabet without hopping on the letter with the stone. For fun, you can also hop the alphabet backwards!

Tip: If your child is just learning to read, say the sound each letter makes. Older kids can say a word that begins with that letter.

What You'll Need:

- Download the BINGO template (see the link below)
- Contact paper
- Scissors
- Dry erase or washable markers or crayons
- Coins or chocolate kisses
- Computer and printer

Arabic Bingo

Bingo is an excellent way to practice your letters and numbers, and a fun way to get your children to begin to recognize the Arabic alphabet and Arabic numbers.

Kid Assembly

Download and print the BINGO templates from www.allahtoz.com/activity-book with the help of a grown-up. Laminate the cards with contact paper and trim the sides with scissors, leaving a ½" border for more durability.

How to Play

The object of the game is to cover or make off five squares in a row (diagonally, horizontally, or vertically) that have been called by the leader.

Using dry erase or washable markers, coins or chocolates, mark the letter or number the leader calls out. Continue marking the letters or numbers until someone yells "BINGO." If you're playing with chocolates, the winner can eat her game pieces as a prize!

Tip: It is easier to shake and find the letters if the bottle is not completely full.

What You'll Need:

- Clear plastic empty water bottle with all labels removed

- About 1-2 cups of rice

- Glue

- ¾" x ¾" colorful plastic cubes (see appendix)

- Black permanent marker

- Small funnel, or roll up a piece of paper into a cone and tape it

- Pencil and paper

"I Spy" Alphabet Shaker

These shakers are great toys for all ages. All you need is an empty bottle, some rice or sand, and any knick knacks you may want to add.
To practice Arabic letters, use store-bought letter charms or create your own letter blocks. They will help develop your child's recognition of the symbols, and guide them towards literacy as well as hone his or her motor skills by manipulating the plastic bottle to find letters inside.
It's like a scavenger hunt in a bottle.

Kid Assembly

On each small block or cube, carefully write one Arabic letter on all 4 sides with permanent marker. Place on scrap paper to dry, as to not get ink on other surfaces.

Fill it Up!

Fill the bottle ¼ full with rice. Drop several cubes into the bottle, then add another layer of rice. Continue the rotation by alternating adding cubes and layers of rice. Make sure to place all the cubes inside and leave 2" of empty space at the top.

To permanently seal, put a ring of glue around the inside of the lid, then place the lid tightly on the bottle. For added protection, use packing or duct tape around the top of the bottle and lid.

Record Your Data

For older children, have your child write down all the letters they find on a paper.

What You'll Need:

- A wooden tray, glass platter or a shallow plastic bin with at least two inches on the sides (to prevent spilling)

- A colorful variety of play sand (see appendix)

Letters in the Sand

Writing in the sand is a fun way for your child to learn their letters! It's the perfect medium for new writers and can be reused over and over. Have your child practice letters, numbers and shapes with this colorful tray and make learning fun.

Kid Assembly

Put in a generous amount of play sand into the tray, covering the entire bottom at least 1/4 inch with a two-inch tray. You can add a little glitter to make it sparkly!

Practice writing Arabic letters in the sand with your finger. Shake the tray gently to erase the sand. Start over with another letter.

Tip: Take it to the next level by copying prewritten letters, or get quizzed by writing the letters a grown-up calls out!

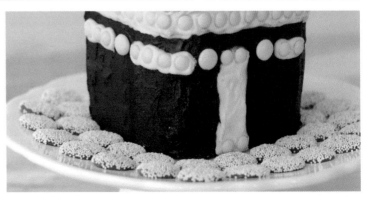

Islam

Islam is the second most popular religion in the world. It means submission to Allah, obeying all His orders, and worshiping Him alone. It is a religion of love, peace, compassion, mercy, and justice.

Followers of Islam are called Muslims. Islam calls on all Muslims to support one another, and strives for a strong, united community.

Muslims follow five basic pillars to have a pious existence:

- The **Shahadah** which is believing in one and only God, and that the Prophet Muhammad (SAW) was the messenger of God.
- **Salah** which is remembering and worshiping God five times a day.
- **Fasting** during the holy month of Ramadan.
- **Zakat** which is giving to charity a part of your savings.
- Going on the pilgrimage to Mecca, called **Hajj,** at least once in your life.

Teach your children the basic fundamentals of Islam at an early age by incorporating the five pillars into part of your everyday routines.

What You'll Need:
- Any color plain t-shirt (see appendix)
- Fabric paint
- Glue gun
- Needle and thread
- Sequins, lace, ribbons, transfer letters, or other embellishments to add to your shirt

. . . .

Homemade Designer Islamic T-shirts

Let your child share his faith with his family and friends by decorating t-shirts with fun Islamic phrases and designs that can be worn to school, camp, or the park. Your children will love to model their custom-made t-shirts to the world!

Kid Assembly
Choose from a variety of phrases and designs to decorate your t-shirt (see below for examples). Use the glue gun and needle with the help of a grown-up.

Make it Your Own Ideas
Crescent and star designs
"Happy Ramadan"
"I love Islam"
Super Muslim logo

"A is for ALLAH"
"I am fasting"
"American Muslim Girl" logo
A Kaaba or mosque design

See www.AllahToZ.com/activity-book.com for more ideas!

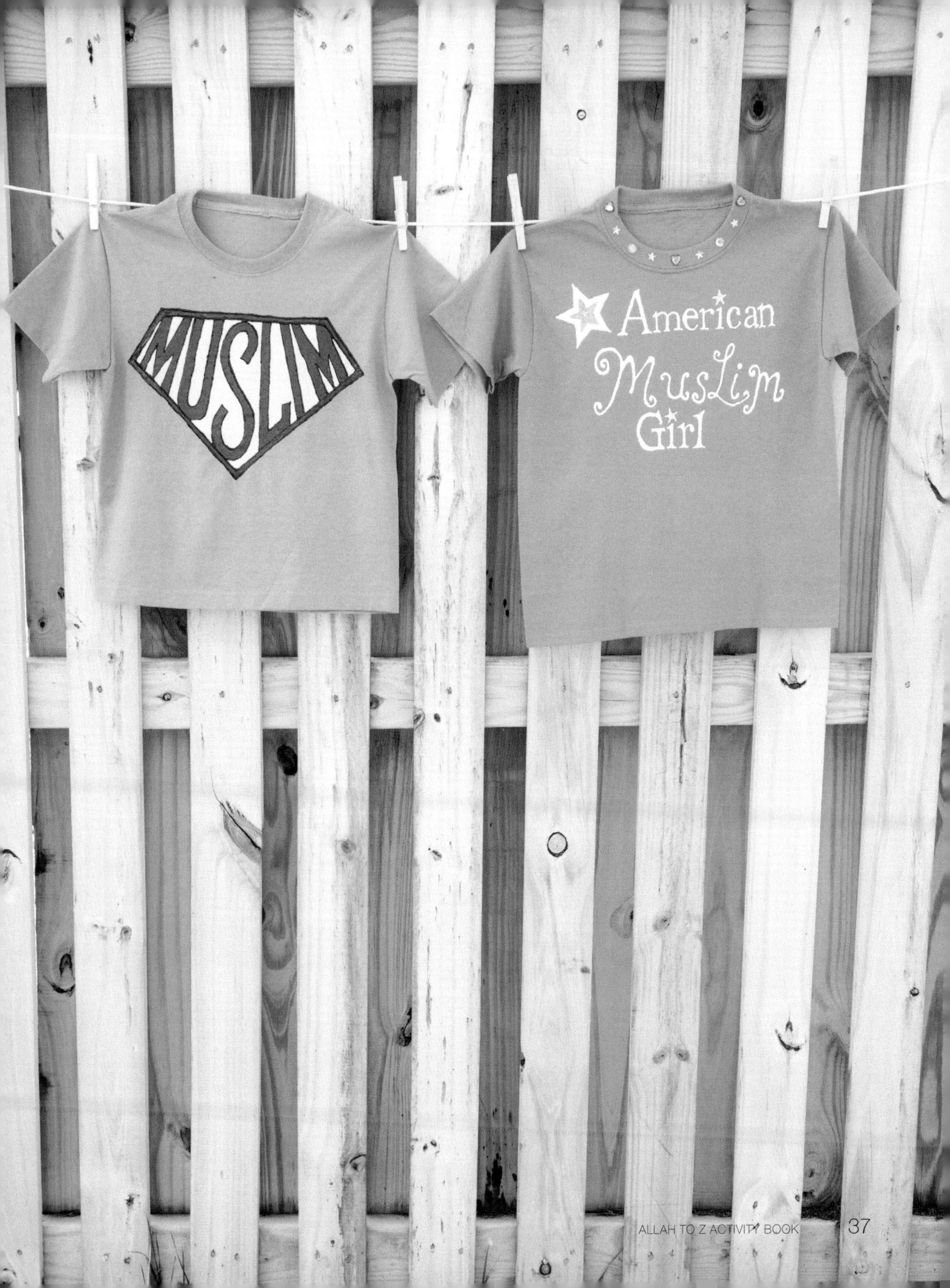
MUSLIM
American
Muslim
Girl

- Cube gift box, or an empty and sterilized milk carton cut in half
- Black paint, acrylic works best
- Yellow or gold paint
- White paint
- Paint brushes
- Pencil & Ruler
- Craft knife

Kaaba Bank

Teach your child to donate a portion of their allowance every Jummah (referring to a day of gathering, usually traditional Friday prayers), or have them collect coins all year long and donate during Ramadan with their very own Kaaba bank.

Kid Assembly

Using a ruler and pencil, mark a 2" long line and a ¼" wide line on the top, center of the box, to fit bills and coins. Cut each line open with a craft knife.

Paint the sides and bottom of the box with black paint. Let it dry completely, then give it one to two more coats of paint. Let it dry completely.

Paint the top of the box white.

Paint a solid yellow line all the way around the box, 2" down from the top of the box. Paint a dash and dotted yellow line under the solid line, leaving ½" of black space between the 2 lines.

On one side of the box on the left, paint a long rectangle with yellow paint for the Kaaba door (see picture). Let it dry completely.

Start collecting!

What You'll Need:

- Colorful yarn
- Scissors
- Cardstock
- Pencil
- Glue

Yarn Art

Create colorful masterpieces worth framing while teaching Islamic facts and history. Your child can make any image they'd like with the yarn. This project is simple and easy and yet can have intricate and fabulous results.

Kid Assembly

Trace your design from one of the templates listed in the appendix such as the mosque or crescent and stars, or create your own, onto the cardstock.

Cut pieces of yarn and glue the yarn onto the cardstock, working in small sections, following your design.

Frame your finished piece and hang it on the wall!

What You'll Need:

- A variety of 33 colorful beads, 2 separating beads, and 3 end beads
- Stretch Magic bead and jewelry cord, cut to your desired length
- Glue

Make your own Tasbeeh

The two common methods of keeping count of Tasbeeh, Tahmeed, and Takbeer are counting on the joints of the fingers, or counting the beads on a Tasbeeh, 33 times each. It is always best to say dhikr on your fingers, but making a Tasbeeh is a fun and creative way for your child to work on their fine motor skills. Imagine how proud your child will feel when praying with his or her own created Tasbeeh, especially when on the go.

Kid Assembly

Begin by stringing 11 beads onto your cord, then adding one separating bead. Continue to string 11 more beads, and one separating bead. String your last 11 beads. Bring the 2 ends of the cord together and string your three end beads. Tie two tight knots at the end and seal the knot with glue.

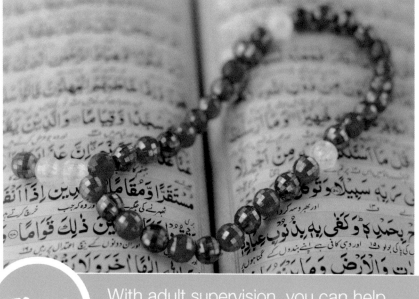

Tip: With adult supervision, you can help your child make a Tasbeeh bracelet by using smaller beads!

What You'll Need:

- Printing paper
- Computer & printer
- Scissors
- Binder clip

Salah Flip Book

Teach your child the basic salah positions with this fun salah flip book!

Kid Assembly

Download the salah pages at www.AllahToZ.com/activity-book, print on printer paper (thinner paper will flip better than cardstock) and cut on the dotted lines.

To put all the pages in the right order for viewing, the book should begin with the last page: you flip from back to front. Seal the pages with a binder clip, staples or punch in holes and tie with a colorful ribbon.

Start Flipping!

Blessing Bag

This is a great project to initiate during Ramadan and continue all year long. It can also fill homeschool community service hours that some states require. By having children fill up bags and creating special cards, they will understand that not everyone may be as blessed as they are and will feel proud of themselves as they do these good deeds.

Kid Assembly

Some ideas to use to fill up your bag:

- Re-sealable plastic sandwich or quart size bag
- Small bottled water
- Trail mix, crackers, granola bars, pretzels, applesauce, etc.
- Bandages

- Toothbrush and toothpaste
- Tissues
- Travel toiletries, or toiletries you've collected from hotels
- Plastic utensils
- Hand wipes

- Cup of soup packets
- Lip balm
- Homemade cards

Parents help handing them out!

Keep the blessing bags in the car, or during the summer months grab a few bags from inside (as to not have anything melt from the heat) as you head out the door. These bags can be as big or as small as you would like to make them, and every little bit counts. Contact local shelters, food banks and free health care services (both secular and religious) to drop off these bags, or add a card with their addresses inside.

What You'll Need:

- A variety of colors of craft foam

- Scissors

- Pencil

- 5 Brass brads or paper fasteners

- 5x foam number stickers from 1-12 or use marker

- Foam alphabet letter stickers, or use marker

- 5x two clock hands drawn on foam or construction paper – one short, one long, on craft foam

- Glue

• •

Time for Salah!

Have fun making these cool clocks with your kids. They will enjoy learning how to tell time while adjusting the time on the clocks according to the appropriate prayer schedule, either daily or weekly.

Kid Assembly

Trace five circles of any size onto the craft foam and cut out the five circles with the help of a grown-up. Cut out your five long and five short clock hands.

Glue or stick the numbers onto each of the five foam circles, also known as the clock faces.

Stick one brad through both short and long clock hands. Poke the brad through the center of the clock face.

Label each clock with the appropriate prayer name – Fajr, Zuhr, Asr, Maghrib, Isha.

Set the clock according to the appropriate prayer schedule.

Time to Pray!

Fajr

Zuhr

Asr

Maghrib

Isha

What You'll Need:

- Four or five wooded peg dolls (see appendix)

- Pencil

- Small paint brushes

- Gloss enamel paint pots (see appendix) or acrylic paint

- Pieces of felt

- Glue

Painted Muslim Dolls

Your child will love creating these beautiful hand-painted Muslim dolls to play with or to use when recreating scenes from the hajj!

Kid Assembly

Using a pencil, draw eyes, nose, mouth, arms, hands, and clothes on your Muslim dolls.

Paint them using your acrylic paint.

Glue pieces of felt to the wooden dolls to create clothes, hijabs, abayas or hats.

ALLAH TO Z ACTIVITY BOOK

- Pre-made gingerbread pieces or unbroken graham cracker squares

- Square gift box (see appendix on where to buy)

- Frosting tubes in white and yellow

- Peanut butter or an allergy alternative

- Aluminum foil

- One tub of black frosting

- Candy assortments like yellow M&Ms

No-Bake Gingerbread Kaaba

During Ramadan, parents want to create lasting memories with their children, so forget a long day of baking and keep the activity simple and enjoyable for young kids.

Kid Assembly

Cover your box with aluminum foil to keep everything clean.

Spread peanut butter all over the sides of the box, and stick your unbroken graham crackers or gingerbread pieces to the peanut butter to make the walls of the Kaaba. Trim the graham crackers as needed.

Spread white frosting to the roof.

Spread the black frosting around the sides of the Kaaba.

Decorate the Kaaba with yellow frosting tubes all the way around the Kaaba with 2 lines – one solid yellow and one with short lines and dashes.

Create a long rectangle door with yellow frosting to make the door to the Kaaba.

Decorate with yellow M&Ms or sprinkle with yellow or gold sprinkles to make it sparkle!

Let it dry until hardened.

What You'll Need:

- Black construction paper

- Pencil or white chalk

- Scissors or craft knife with a grown-up watching

- A variety of colors of tissue paper, cut up into one inch squares

- Contact paper or clear paper protector covers

- Glue stick

- Tape

Stained Glass Mosque

Share the month of Ramadan with your neighbors by decorating your windows with homemade stained glass Islamic art. They will capture the sunlight beautifully and your child will learn to explore light and color in a creative way.

Kid Assembly

Trace a template design (see appendix) or create your own design using pencil or white chalk on black construction paper. Carefully cut out the design with a grown-up helping, using scissors or craft knife.

Stick different color pieces of tissue paper to the contact paper, or glue the tissue paper to a clear paper protector cover.

Glue or tape the contact paper or clear paper protector cover with the colored tissue paper to the black construction paper, trimming the ends as needed around the design.

Frame onto your window and let the sun shine through!

Eid

The two major holidays for Muslims are **Eid-ul-Fitr** and **Eid-al-Adha.**

Eid-ul-Fitr celebrates the end of Ramadan.

Eid-al-Adha, celebrates the sacrifice that Prophet Ibrahim was willing to make of his own son, Ismael.

Muslims celebrate these holidays in several ways. We enjoy large feasts with friends and family, attend Eid prayer, dress up in new clothes and decorate our homes with beautiful lights and decorations.

Make Eid special for your children from a very early age. Create memories with them that will remind everyone how much fun it is to spend holidays with family and friends.

What You'll Need:

- 1 apple, peeled and chopped into 1" pieces

- 2 tablespoons butter, melted

- Store bought pie dough, or you can make your own, rolled out and ready to go

- Crescent and star-shaped cookie cutters

- Cinnamon

- Sugar

• •

Crescent and Star Apple Pies

These crescent and star-shaped apple pies are super easy to make and ready in only 10 minutes! This healthy and sweet snack will satisfy your child's sweet tooth and is perfect for your next Eid party.

Kid Assembly

Using your cookie cutters, cut out eight star shapes and eight crescent shapes out of the pie dough.

Using a spoon, gently spread the melted butter on top of four star and four crescent pieces of dough.

Fill the four stars and four crescent dough pieces with the chopped apples.

Lightly sprinkle with a pinch of cinnamon and sugar.

Top the four star dough pieces with the remaining four star dough pieces. Top the four crescent dough pieces with the remaining four crescent dough pieces.

Using your fingers, pinch the sides closed.

Add a few dribbles of butter and a pinch of sugar to the top of the pies.

Place on a cookie dough sheet and with a grown-up helping, bake at 350 (F) degrees for 10 minutes, with more or less time depending on the thickness of your pie dough.

What You'll Need:

- Colorful glitter or plain craft foam

- Colorful twine or string

- Star and crescent cookie cutters or templates (see appendix)

- Scissors

- Glue sticks

- Hole punch

. . . .

Eid Mobile

Hung in your doorway, windowsill or on top of the dining table, the crescent and star mobile is easy to make and a colorful way to decorate for Eid. It will look so inviting you may end up making more than one!

Kid Assembly

Trace one large crescent from the template listed in the appendix onto glitter or plain craft foam. Cut out the crescent.

Trace three small stars from the template listed in the appendix onto glitter or plain craft foam. Cut out the stars.

Punch holes onto the crescent where you would like the stars to hang and connect three stars to the crescent with the string, two on one string, and one on the other string. Knot the ends.

Find the center of the top of the moon (the center is where you will punch the hole for the entire mobile to hang straight). Once you have this center, punch a hole about 1/4 inch from the edge and use a string to hang the mobile.

What You'll Need:

- Any cake recipe or store bought cake
- Can of icing
- Sprinkles
- Letter and shape cookie cutters

Easy Eid Cake

Children love helping in the kitchen and this cake is so easy to make and fun to decorate.

Kid Assembly

Spread icing onto the top of your cake.

Gently lay your E I D letter cookie cutters and star-shaped cookie cutters where you want.

Scoop the sprinkles into the cookie cutter cutouts. Carefully lift off the cookie cutters.

What You'll Need:

- Colorful construction paper
- Scissors
- Stapler
- Ruler
- Decorations such as markers, stickers, paint, gemstones, glitter

- -

Eid Lanterns

This easy Eid lantern project, also called fanoos in Arabic, is made from paper. Paper lanterns are very popular with children during celebrations in Islamic countries and these paper lanterns are so simple to make and lots of fun to decorate!

Kid Assembly

Take one piece of construction paper and fold the paper in half, lengthwise. Use scissors with a grownup watching and cut slits into the folded edge, leaving 1-2" of space at the top.

Unfold the paper and decorate as you would like with markers, stickers, glitter or paint.

Loosely roll it up into a tube lengthwise. Staple the ends together.

Cut a small strip of construction paper, about 5" long and 1" wide, to be used as a handle. Attach each end to the lantern and staple it to the lantern.

Create many different, colorful lanterns and hang them everywhere!

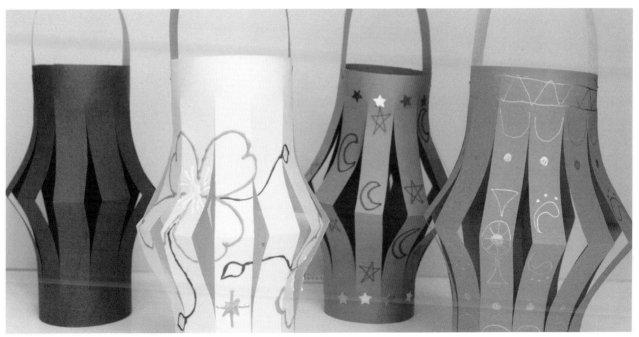

What You'll Need:

- 1-2 packs of 4" x 9" clear treat bags
- An assortment of candies and chocolate
- Stickers, stamps
- Bubbles, play dough
- Pencils
- Dollar store goodies
- Any color cardstock paper
- Markers, crayons, glitter, glue
- Scissors
- Stapler

Eid Treat Bags

Celebrate Eid with friends and family by having your children hand out these yummy Eid treat bags after Eid Prayer at your local mosque or at an Eid party!

Kid Assembly

Fill up your treat bags halfway with a variety of fillings; candy, chocolate, stamps, stickers, Eid Fun Pencils, bubbles, play dough, etc.

Fold in half and seal the bag with a homemade "bag tag".

Bag Tag

Depending on the size of your bag, cut the cardstock paper to fit the size of the top of the bag, or 4" long by 4" if you use a 4 x 9" treat bag.

Fold in half and write "Eid Mubarak" and decorate with markers, glitter and stickers on one side. Decorate the other side as you wish, or include the recipients' name. Fit the folded cardstock over the opening of the bag and staple shut.

What You'll Need:

- A bunch of #2 pencils
- White 4x6 address labels
- Craft knife, ruler and cutting surface or scissors
- Markers
- Pencil to mark with
- Glue stick

Eid Fun Pencils

No need to order custom pencils for your next Eid party! Use white mailing labels to print and personalize, or hand-write a special message.

Kid Assembly

With a pencil and grown-up help, lightly mark 1 1/8" wide strips. This will be the size that will fit around a standard Number 2 pencil.

Decorate the paper with Eid designs and phrases.

Cut the strips with scissors. Remove the label from the backing and starting towards the eraser end of the pencil, stick on the end of the label, aligning the straight edge with the metal part of the pencil.

Smooth the label down the length of the pencil and run a glue stick along the seam to seal the label. Sharpen the pencil to remove the little bit of the exposed pencil left on the bottom.

Tip: If you are computer savvy, open a word processing application document and create custom labels and print them out. Or use markers to color them in, write "Eid Mubarak" and/or the child's name.

What You'll Need:

- Pencil
- Colorful construction paper
- Scissors
- Brown marker

Henna Hands

For many children, Eid festivities are not complete without painting henna on their hands. This craft lets your child practice drawing different designs on their own handprints. Once they pick a design they love, transfer that design over to their real hands for Eid with real henna.

Kid Assembly

Trace your hands onto the construction paper using a pencil.

Draw your henna-inspired designs. Some designs you can choose are suns, flowers, Arabic scripts, vines, dots and lines.

Cut out your handprints and mount onto a different color construction paper. Don't forget to date the back!

APPENDIX

Where To Buy

The following is a list of vendors we work with on our projects for our tools, materials, and craft supplies.

- A.C. Moore
- Amazon
- CVS
- Michaels
- M&J Trimmings

- Target
- The Container Store
- The Yarn Company
- Your Local Supermarket

Templates and Clip Art

To download the templates and clip art for the following projects, please go to our website at **www.AllahToZ.com/activity-book**. Unless otherwise indicated, templates may be printed on standard copy paper.

- Oreo Lunar Calendar moon phases and diagram
- Random Acts of Ramadan Kindness card template
- Crescent and Star Pillows shape template
- Good Deed Tree Leaf template
- Arabic Alphabet Cookies letters
- Arabic Bingo Game Template download
- Homemade Designer Islamic T-shirts variations
- Yarn Art template
- Salah Flip Book download
- Stained Glass Mosque template
- Eid Mobile crescent and star template

Printed in Poland
by Amazon Fulfillment
Poland Sp. z o.o., Wrocław